Mad 4 Maths
2nd Class

Len and Ann Frobisher

© Len and Anne Frobisher 2002
Under Licence from Pearson Education Limited
Original title published as Maths Plus Word Problems

This edition published in 2012 by Gill & Macmillan
Hume Avenue
Park West
Dublin 12
http://www.gillmacmillan.ie

Designers: Bookcraft Ltd, Stroud, Gloucestershire and M & J Graphics, Harold's Cross, Dublin

Illustrators: Garry Davies and Nicola Sedgwick

ISBN: 978-1-84450-140-3

Contents

UNIT	TOPIC	PAGE

Autumn 1ˢᵗ half term

1	Number problems 1	4
2	Number problems 2	5
3	Number problems 3	6
4	Money problems 1	7
5	Length problems 1	8
6	Time problems 1	9
7	Review problems 1	10

Autumn 2ⁿᵈ half term

8	Number problems 4	12
9	Number problems 5	13
10	Money problems 2	14
11	Number problems 6	15
12	Length problems 2	16
13	Time problems 2	17
14	Review problems 2	18

Spring 1ˢᵗ half term

1	Number problems 7	19
2	Number problems 8	20
3	Money problems 3	21
4	Number problems 9	22
5	Time problems 3	23
6	Weight problems 1	24
7	Review problems 3	25

Spring 2ⁿᵈ half term

8	Number problems 10	26
9	Number problems 11	27
10	Money problems 4	28
11	Number problems 12	29
12	Money problems 5	30
13	Measures problems 1	31
14	Review problems 4	32

Summer 1ˢᵗ half term

1	Number problems 13	3
2	Number problems 14	35
3	Money problems 6	36
4	Number problems 15	37
5	Capacity problems 1	38
6	Time problems 4	39
7	Review problems 5	40

Summer 2ⁿᵈ half term

8	Number problems 16	42
9	Number problems 17	43
10	Money problems 7	44
11	Number problems 18	45
12	Money problems 8	46
13	Measures problems 2	47
14	Review problems 6	48

Number problems 1

1 A number is falling off.

What number is falling off?

2 Jack has a tube of 6 Sunbursts and a tube of 3 sunbursts.

How many Sunbursts does Jack have altogether?

3 There are 5 fish in each tank.

How many fish are in the two tanks?

4 Ciara has 4 packs of crayons.

How many crayons does Ciara have?

5 Mark counts in tens.

10, 20, 30, 40

What number should Mark say next?

6 The bus numbers go down in tens.

What will be the next number on the last bus?

7

I am 2 more than 5.

What am I?

Number problems 2

1 A supermarket has 47 check-outs. One is closed.

How many are open?

2 At St. Enda's school 73 children are ill.

Write 73 in words.

3 There are 63 people waiting for a ride.
Ten more join the line.

How many are there now?

4 There are 7 balloons at a party.
Pat bursts 4 of them.

How many are left?

5 Lucy has 18 toy cars.

Ben has half as many as Lucy.
How many cars has Ben?

6 Nine children like red apples best. Two children like green apples best.

How many more like red apples than green ones?

7

I am 10 less than 17.

What am I?

Number problems 3

1 Harry bakes 27 buns. He puts two lots of 10 into boxes.

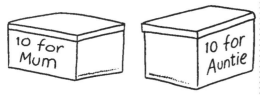

How many buns are left?

2 There are 36 people on a bus. Then 9 more get on.

How many are on the bus now?

3 There are 53 children in the pool. Eleven of them are boys.

How many are girls?

4 There are 10 biscuits in a pack.

Altogether how many biscuits are in 7 packs?

5 Ronan has 7 cards. Tom has double that.

How many cards has Tom?

6 A stall has 46 story books. It sells 9 of them.

How many are left?

7

I am in the 10 times tables. I am between 65 and 75. What am I?

Money problems 1

1 Bill has €2. His dad gives him €1. His mum gives him 50c.

How much does Bill have now?

2 A spaceship costs €8. A rocket costs €7.

How much does it cost to buy both of them?

3 Zoe buys some chews. They cost 3c each.

What is the cost of 10 chews?

4 A pencil costs 7c. A rubber costs 2c.

How much does Stacey need to buy both?

5 Orla has €4. She buys a comic for €1.

How much has Orla left?

6 In one pocket Alan has a 5c coin. In his other pocket he has three 1c coins.

He spends 6c.
How much has he left?

7

I am a gold coin. I am more than 10c and less than 50c.

What am I?

Length problems 1

1 Greg makes a kite that is 45 cm long. Fionn makes one that is 40 cm long.

Who makes the longer kite? How much longer is it?

2 Ciara hops 2 metres then jumps 4 metres.

Altogether how far does Ciara hop and jump?

3 Tommy has a rubber that is 3 cm long. Lucy's rubber is twice as long as Tommy's.

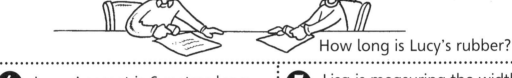

How long is Lucy's rubber?

4 James' carpet is 6 metres long. He cuts some off so it is 5 metres long.

What length does he cut off?

5 Lisa is measuring the width of her table.

What unit of length do you think she should use?

6 Luke's tower is 10 cm tall. he knocks 3 cm off the top. Then he adds some more blocks to make it 2 cm taller.

How tall is the tower now?

7

I am double one metre.

What am I?

Time problems 1

1 Stephen leaves school at 3 o'clock.

He takes 15 minutes to walk home. At what time does Stephen get home?

2 Eoin goes on a ferry. He sleeps for 4 hours of the journey and is awake for 5 hours.

How long is the journey?

3 Alex balances a ball on his head for 18 seconds. Liam does it for only half this time.

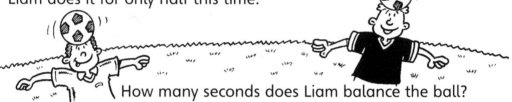

How many seconds does Liam balance the ball?

4 Ten children take turns to read a book for charity. Each child reads for 5 minutes.

What is the total time for the ten children?

5 Rob and Rachel stand on one leg. Rob does it for 2 minutes, Rachel does it for 5 minutes.

How much longer does Rachel stand on one leg than Rob?

6 Ann and John go on holiday. They spend one day with their aunt, then 7 days with their grandparents. It rains on 4 days.

On how many days of the holiday does it not rain?

7

I am a whole number of hours. I am between half-past 10 and half-past 11.

What am I?

Toffee apples 7c
Candy floss 10c

10 Sparklers
10 Sparklers
10 Sparklers
10 Sparklers

1. How many children are at the bonfire?
   How many grown-ups are there?
   Altogether how many people are at the bonfire?

2. How many sparklers are in each box?
   How many boxes of sparklers are on the table?
   How many sparkers are there altogether?

3. At the start there were 10 toffee apples for sale.
   How many are left on the stall?
   How many have been sold?

4. Mrs O'Leary buys 7 candy floss with a €1 coin.
   What do they cost?
   How much change does she get?

5. Here are 2 rockets.
   Which rocket is longer?
   How many centimetres longer?

6. The Shooter rocket goes 10 metres high.
   The Blaster rocket goes to half this height.
   How high does the Blaster go?

7. The bonfire starts at 6 o'clock.
   It will end at 8 o'clock.
   How long will the bonfire last?

8. Mrs O'Brien brought 11 fireworks.
   Mr Murphy brought 13 fireworks.
   How many did they bring altogether?

9. The Magic Fountain shoots stars 2 metres high.
   How many centimetres is that?

10. The Vulcan shoots stars 10 cm higher than
    the Magic Fountain.
    How high do its stars go?

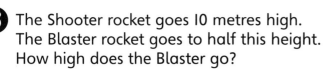

Number problems 4

1 The number on Diarmaid's house has fallen off.

What should the number be?

2 One of the balls has an odd number.

What is the odd number?

3 The seat numbers go down in 10s.

What is the hidden seat number?

4 The numbers on the hooks should be odd.

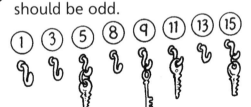

What number is not correct?
What should the number be?

5 The chalets are numbered with even numbers.

What is the number of the chalet behind the tree?

6 Anna counts in 10s starting at 4.

4 , 14 , 24 , 34 , 44 ...

What number should Anna say next?

7

I am three 10s more than 21.

What am I?

Number problems 5

1 Sinéad has 52 picture cards. Ryan has 55 cards.

Who has more cards?
How many more?

2 Aoife has 41 books on her shelf and Ben has 38 on his shelf.

Who has more books?
How many more?

3 On a boat trip Jamie sees 2 whales. Later he sees another 8 whales.

How many whales does he see altogether?

4 For a school trip children are put into 10 groups. Each group has 6 children.

How many children go on the trip?

5 Five children line up in order. Two of them are in the wrong places.

Which two are in the wrong places?

6 These are the riders in a race.

John is third.
What is his number?

7

I am half-way between 10 and 20.

What am I?

Money problems 2

1 Ian collects 1 cent coins.
He puts them in boxes of 100.

How many cent has he in his
4 boxes?
How much is this in €?

2 Molly's dad says, 'If you save
€12, I will double it.'

How much will Molly have
after her dad has doubled
her €12?

3 Ciarán buys a 14c choc bar and a
6c apple.

What is the total cost of the choc
bar and the apple?

4 Toy penguins cost €4 each.
Anne's mum buys 10 to put
in a parade.

How much do the 10 penguins
cost?

5 Colm buys the stickers with a 20c coin.

How much change does Colm get?

6 Laura is given five €1 coins for her birthday.

How many cent is her money worth?

7

*I am the smallest
gold coin.*

What am I?

Number problems 6

1 There are 25 sheep in a field. Eleven more sheep are put in the field.

How many sheep are in the field now?

2

How many wheels on I trike?
How many wheels on 5 trikes?

3 Ellen thinks each person at her party will eat 2 biscuits.

There will be 6 people. How many biscuits does she need to make?

4 In a wood there were 34 trees. Eleven of the trees were blown over in a storm.

How many were left standing?

5 Seán eats half a bar of chocolate. Hannah eats the other half.

How much of the chocolate is left?

6 Alex builds 7 sandcastles. Meghan builds twice as many as Alex.

How many does she build?

7

I am an odd two-digit number. My digits add to make 3.

What am I?

Length problems 2

1 A pile of computer games is 12 cm high. Another pile is 13 cm high.

How high would the games be if they were in one pile?

2 A railway engine and its tender are 15 metres long. The engine is 9 metres long.

How long is the tender?

3 This table shows the heights of four children.

name	height
Will	119 cm
Erin	120 cm
Daniel	116 cm
Tara	122 cm

Who is the tallest?
Who is the shortest?

4 A line of boys is 15 metres long. A line of girls is 16 metres long.

If the girls and boys make one line, how long will it be?

5 Nicola's left foot is just 17½ cm long.

What is the length of Nicola's left foot to the nearest cm?

6 A hall is 18 metres long. The dining room is 9 metres lor

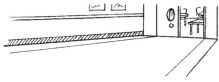

What is the total length of the hall and the dining room?

7

I am a length in cm. Both my digits are even and they add to make 4.

What am I?

Time problems 2

1 The table shows the birthdays of five children.

name	birthday
Seán	30 March
Lucy	11 December
Aoife	4 July
Cormac	22 May
Harry	8 October

Whose birthday is last every year?
Whose birthday comes third every year?

2 Shannon looks at the clock. In half an hour she must leave for school.

At what time must Shannon leave for school?

3 Conor writes his full name in 20 seconds. Anna writes hers in half the time.

How long does it take for Anna to write her name?

4 Ten people cycle for 30 hours in a relay race. Each one cycles for the same length of time.

For how long does each person cycle?

5 Charlie looks at the clock. In 15 minutes it is lunchtime.

`12:00`

What time is lunch?

6 The clock shows the end of silent reading. It lasted for half an hour.

At what time did silent reading start?

7

*I am a time in the morning.
My number of hours is 10.
My number of minutes is half of 60.*

What am I?

Review problems 2

1 In First Class there are 48 children. There are 52 in Second Class.

How many children are there altogether in First and Second Class?

2 Sinéad has a €20 note. She buys an €11 jigsaw.

How much change does she get?

3 Rebecca's baby sister is 47 cm when born.
She grows 9 cm in the next 3 months.

How long is she then?

4 Seán gets home from school at 4 o'clock. It takes him half an hour.

At what time does he leave school?

5 There are 3 ducks on a pond. Five more ducks fly in and 2 ducks fly away.

How many ducks are then on the pond?

6 Molly has saved €24. She is given another €23 for her birthday.

How much has she now?

7

When 11 is added to me the answer is 20.

What am I?

Number problems 7

1 There are 2 buns in each box.

How many buns are in 6 boxes?

2 In a game Jack scores 8 points.

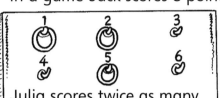

Julia scores twice as many points as Jack.
How many points does Julia score?

3 On each sheet there are 10 stamps.

How many stamps are on 3 sheets?

4 Eoin counts up in 3s.

three, six, nine.

Which is the first multiple of 5 that Eoin says?

5 Katie cuts each cake into 5 pieces.

  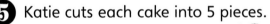

How many pieces are there altogether?

6 In a swimming pool there are 10 children.
Seven of them get out and 3 more get in.

How many are in the pool now?

7

I am a multiple of 5.
The sum of my 2 digits is 8.

What am I?

Number problems 8

1 On a bus there are 6 passengers.
At a stop 2 more get on.
At the next stop 7 more get on.

How many are on the bus now?

2 There are 81 fish in Dylan's tank
In Jane's tank there are 69 fish.

Whose tank has more fish?
How many more?

3 At a bus station there are
10 buses. Half of the buses are
double-deckers.

How many of the buses are
double-deckers?

4 At Terminal 1 there are 47 planes.
At Terminal 2 there are 62 planes.

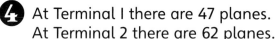

How many planes are there altogether?

5 On a day trip there are 16 people.
One-half of them are children.

How many are children?

6 A boat can carry 8 people.

A full boat makes 10 journeys.
How many people does it
carry altogether?

7

*I am more than 20 and less than 30.
The difference between my digits is 5.* What am I?

Money problems 3

1 Roisín buys one toffee bar and one chew.

What is the total cost?

2 Hannah gave the shopkeeper a €10 note. She was given a €5 note as change.

How much did Hannah spend at the shop?

3 Peter has one 10c coin and two 5c coins in his pocket.

How much has Peter in his pocket?

4 A red T-shirt costs €6 and a white one costs €3.

How much more does the red T-shirt cost than the white one?

5 At the Summer Fair Grace buys an 8c bun and a 2c drink.

How much does she pay altogether?

6 Brian has a 20c coin.
He buys a tube of Fizzers for 10c.
Later he finds 5c that he had lost.

How much does he have now?

7

I am the sum of one of each of the copper coins.

What am I?

Number problems 9

1 A bus has 8 people upstairs and 6 people downstairs.

How many people are on the bus?

2 Each car on the ride can carry 4 people.

How many people can 2 cars carry?

3 Caoimhe buys 2 bunches of flowers.
One bunch has 6 flowers, the other has 9 flowers.

How many flowers does Caoimhe buy?

4 Each basketball team has 5 players and I reserve.

How many children are there altogether in two teams?

5 Zoe buys 2 bags of carrots.
One bag has 22 carrots, the other has 23 carrots.

How many carrots does Zoe have altogether?

6 In a marina there are 9 boats. Seven more boats sail in.

How many are in the marina now?

7

I am an even number. My tens digit is 6 less than my units digit.

What am I?

Time problems 3

1 A boat journey across the Irish Sea takes exactly one whole day.

How many hours is the journey?

2 One Monday Susan says that in 9 days she will go on holiday.

On what day will she go on holiday?

3 Second Class have I hour in which to make a model castle.

How many minutes do they have?

4 It took Liam 60 seconds to put on his shoes.

How long was that in minutes?

5 In II hours time the Smith family fly to Disneyland.

What time will the clock show when they fly?

6 Ten children have the same amount of time on a swing. Altogether they spend 60 minutes on the swing.

How long is each child on the swing?

7

I am the number of months in 2 years.

What am I?

Weight problems 1

1 A box of apples weighs 22 kg.
Then 9 kg of apples are sold.

What is the weight of apples left in the box?

2 Siobhán weighs 5 kg of potatoes.
She puts another 2 kg of potatoes
on the scales.

How many kilograms are on the scales?

3 Tom buys 5 Choco bars.

What is the total weight of the
5 bars?

4 Ava weighs 48 g of flour.
She takes 11 g of flour
off the scales.

How many grams of flour
are left?

5 A large bag of sugar weighs 8 kg.

How many 2 kg bags can be
filled from the large bag?

6 Sophie buys 2 bags of pears.
One weighs 6 kg, the other 2 kg.

What is the difference in the
weights of the bags?

7

*I am less than 80 kg and
more than 70 kg. The difference
between my digits is 5.*

What am I?

Review problems 3

1 There are 100 paper clips in each box.

Altogether how many paper clips are in the 10 boxes?

2 Shay leaves school at 3 o'clock. Seven hours later he flies on a plane to see his grandparents.

At what time does Shay fly?

3 Mary pays for the magazine with a €2 coin.

How much change does she get?

4 The O'Donnell family of 11 adults and 9 children visit Sealife Centre.

How many are there in the O'Donnell family altogether?

5 Clodagh has two money boxes. She writes labels to show how much they hold.

How much has she altogether in the two boxes?

6 Leo weighs 17 kg.
Karl weighs 21 kg.

What would the scales show if they stood on them together?

7

I am four 10s more than 3.

What am I?

Number problems 10

1 At lunch time there are 24 children in the playground.
Ten more children join them.

How many are in the playground now?

2 Each pack of pens has 5 red ones and 5 blue ones.

How many red pens are in 3 packs?
How many blue pens are in 3 packs?
Altogether how many pens are in 3 packs?

3 There are 6 cards in each packet

How many cards are in 2 packet

4 In Second Class there are 41 children.
In First Class there are 10 fewer children.

How many children are in First Class?

5 Two groups of children have tennis lessons. In each lesson there are 9 children.

How many children have lessons?

6 Oisín has 4 boxes of marbles.
There are 5 marbles in each bo

Tony has 10 fewer marbles than Oisín.
How many marbles has Tony?

7

I am in the 2 times tables.
I am between 10 and 30. I am in the count in 5s sequence.

What am I?

Number problems 11

1 Orla saw 77 butterflies at a butterfly farm. Leo saw 53.

Who saw more?
How many more?
Who saw fewer?
How many fewer?

2 At the Spring Fair there were 2 rides for children over 6 years old and 6 rides for all ages.

How many rides were there altogether?

3 The numbers on the houses go up in ones. Some numbers have worn off.

Which numbers are missing?

4 There are 16 dogs each in its own kennel. Nineteen kennels are empty.

How many kennels are there altogether?

5 On sports day the children are put into 10 teams. There are 10 children in each team.

Altogether how many children are in the teams?

6 Danny puts out 34 biscuits on plates. Nineteen of them are eaten.

How many biscuits are left?

7

When you take 8 from me you get 12.

What am I?

Money problems 4

1 Seán has 30c. He spends 23c.

How much change does he get?

2 Laura has €7.
She buys a book for €6.

How much has Laura left?

3 Grace has two purses.
In one purse she has 25c,
in the other she has 32c.

How much does Grace
have altogether?

4 A packet of dog biscuits cost 50c.

How much would 3 packets cost?

5 Alan has two €1 coins, one 50c
coin and two 20c coins.

Which coins should he use to buy
the comic?

6

What is the total cost of the
2 rubbers?

7

*I am the largest
value coin.*

What am I?

Number problems 12

1 A book shop has 11 copies of *Magic for 7 Year Olds* on a shelf and 9 copies on display.

How many copies does it have altogether?

2 Sue and Ronan share equally the 8 cherries in the bowl.

How many cherries do they each get?

3 Amy has 22 toy animals. She gives half of them to her little brother.

How many does she give to her brother?

4 Dad blows up 15 balloons. He gives each child 5 balloons.

How many children get 5 balloons?

5 20 children visit a zoo. Fourteen of them want to see the snakes.

How many do not want to see the snakes?

6 The school has two buses to take 60 children on a visit. Each bus holds the same number of children.

How many children are on each bus?

7

I am 3 less than a half of 20.

What am I?

Money problems 5

1 Áine has 20c. She gives half of it to Darren.

How much has she left?

2 Mum pays €10 for two packs of dice.
There are three dice in each pack.

What is the cost of one pack of dice?

3 Conor has 8c.

He spends a quarter of his 8c.
How much does he spend?

4 Matt has €9. He spends €7 on some flowers for his mum's birthday.

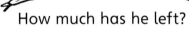

How much has he left?

5 Jenny has 6c. She loses half of it. Her mum then gives her another 4c.

How much has she now?

6 Ryan has saved €4.

He gets €6 for his birthday and spends €5.
How much has he left?

7

I am the total of the smallest and the biggest coins.

What am I?

Measures problems 1

1 A baker has 6 kg of flour. He needs double that amount.

How much flour does the baker need?

2 Eimear has two dogs. One weighs 40 kg, the other weighs 60 kg.

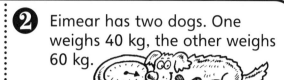

She weighs both dogs together. How many kilograms will the scales show?

3 The station clock shows 8:30.

A train should leave in half an hour. At what time should it leave?

4 On a stall are 10 kg of potatoes. The man sells 4 kg. Then he puts out 3 kg more on the stall.

How many kilograms of potatoes are on the stall now?

5 Amy buys a 70 g pack and a 30 g packet of crisps.

What is the total weight of the two packets?

6 A plane is due to leave at 2:30. It is delayed half an hour.

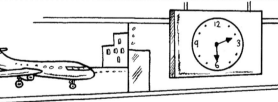

At what time does the plane leave?

7

I am an o'clock. Each of my 2 digits is a straight line.

What am I?

Review problems 4

1 St. Brigid's School visit a farm.
They use 2 buses.
Each bus has 8 adults and 40 children.
How many adults are on the 2 buses?
How many children are on the 2 buses?

2 These are the coins Simon has in his bag.
How much does Simon have?

3 The buses left school at 9:30.
The journey took 45 minutes.
At what time did they arrive at the farm?

4 How many children have got off the white bus at the farm?
How many children are still on the white bus?

5 There are 40 children on the grey bus.
Each of the 8 adults looks after the same number of children.
How many children are with each adult?

6 How many sheep and lambs are in the field?
Tomorrow the farmer will put in 10 more sheep and 16 more lambs.
How many animals will there be in the field then?

7 The black sheep weighs 71 kg. The white sheep weighs 66 kg.
Which sheep is heavier?
How much heavier?

8 Half of the piglets belong to each sow.
How many piglets does each sow have?

9 There are 20 chicks altogether at the farm. Six are outside and the rest are in their house.
How many chicks are in their house?

10 Each tractor has 4 wheels and 1 spare wheel.
How many wheels are there altogether on the 3 tractors?

Number problems 13

1 Tennis balls are in tubes of 3.

How many balls in 5 tubes?

2 A pet shop has cages with 2 gerbils in each.

How many gerbils are in 5 cages?

3 Brendan buys 2 packs of 3 ice-lollies and 2 packs of 4 ice-lollies.

How many lollies does he buy altogether?

4 Second Class play rounders. They are put into 5 teams with 7 children in each team.

How many children are in Second Class?

5 At a railway station there are 9 trains. Eight trains leave the station and 5 more come in.

How many trains are in the station now?

6 Every bag has 4 packets of crisps. Luke buys 4 bags.

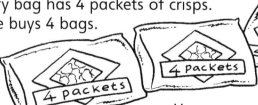

How many packets of crisps does he buy?

7

I am 12 less than 40.

What am I?

Number problems 14

1 Brian's birthday is on the 14th day of the 7th month of the year.

On what date is Brian's birthday?

2 In Second Class, 20 children do not like carrots. Double this number do not like peas.

How many children do not like peas?

3 On a farm visit Aidan guesses that there are 53 hens.

How many is this to the nearest 10?

4 At a barbecue Aoife takes 2 sausages. She later goes back for 7 more.

How many sausages does Aoife have altogether?

5 In a small tank there are 35 fish. In a large tank there are double that number of fish.

How many fish are in the large tank?

6 There are 8 ponies in the stables. Five of them go into the field.

How many are left in the stables?

7

 Add 3 to me and subtract 8 from the answer and you get 22.

What am I?

Money problems 6

1 Lucy has saved €2.30 for her holidays.

In the next few weeks she saves another €1.20
How much has she saved altogether?

2 Philip has €3.70 birthday money.
He spends €1.10 on a toy car.

How much has he left?

3 Rob buys two magazines.
Each costs €1.25.

What is the total cost of the
two magazines?

4 Grandma give her two
grandchildren €3 to share
equally between them.

How much does each
child get?

5 Claire has €5. She is given
another €2. She buys a pair of
socks for €1.80.

How much has she left?

6 Kevin has two €5 notes for his birthday.

He spends €6 on a hurley.
How much has he left?

7

*I am the sum of the
2 smallest value notes.*

What am I?

Number problems 15

1 In a pack there are 8 water bombs.

How many are there in 2 packs?

2 There are 30 people in a cinema queue waiting to see Moon Wars. Nine more join them.

How many are waiting now?

3 At a sports centre there are 70 children on a list for swimming lessons.
Six of them come off the list.

How many are still on the list?

4 Liz scores 35 and 55 points on the game board.

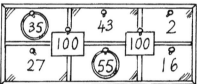

How many points has she scored altogether?

5 There are 10 skittles and a ball in a box. Aaron buys 2 boxes.

How many skittles does Aaron get?

6 A train has 65 passengers. At the first station 14 get off.

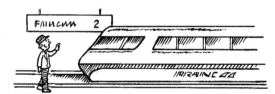

How many are left on the train?

7

When you add 6 to me you get 11.

What am I?

Capacity problems 1

1 A large jug has some juice in it.

Andrew drinks ½ litre of the juice. how much juice is left?

2 A barrel of wine holds 16 litres. It is divided equally between 2 smaller barrels.

How many litres are in each smaller barrel?

3 Maria wants to find out how much water the bath holds.

What would be the best unit of measure?

4 A bottle of Wizer holds 2 litres.

How much do 10 bottles hold?

5 Niamh buys twelve 1 litre bottles of milk.

She divides the 12 bottles equally onto 2 shelve How many litres of milk is on each shelf?

6 Each pack of coke has 10 one-litre cans.

How many litres are in 9 packs?

7

I am less than 60 L and more than 50 L. The sum of my two digits is 9.

What am I?

Time problems 4

1 The clock at the sports hall says 2 o'clock when Eamon and Seán get in the pool.

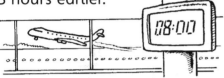

They spend 3 hours in the pool.
At what time do they get out of the pool?

2 Ryan flew on holiday at 08:00. The plane was due to leave 3 hours earlier.

At what time was the plane due to leave?

3 It takes Saoirse 1 hour 30 minutes to get to her Grandma's.

How many minutes altogether does it take Saoirse?

4 Niall's mum looks at the clock when she leaves to go shopping.

She arrives home 2 hours later.
At what time does she arrive home?

5 A train arrived at Cork station at 1 o'clock in the afternoon. It had left Dublin 3 hours earlier.

At what time did the train leave Dublin?

6 It takes 10 children a total of 80 minutes to do a charity relay run. Each child runs for the same number of minutes.

For how long does each child run?

7

I am a digital clock time.
My hours are half of 24.
My minutes are double 15.

What am I?

1 How many more children than adults are in the garden?
How many fewer adults than children are in the garden?

2 The weights of the boys are in the table:

Cormac	28 kg
Nick	35 kg
Brendan	27 kg
Liam	32 kg

Which boy weighs the most?
Which boy is the third heaviest?

3 The Ryan family has 2 adults and 2 children.
They all come late to the barbecue.
When they come, how many people are there altogether?

4 Mr Hogan has 3 packs of herb sausages and
2 packs of spicy sausages to cook.
How many sausages does he have altogether?

4 Herb Sausages
4 Herb Sausages
3 Spicy Sausages
3 Spicy Sausages
4 Herb Sausages

5 Mr O'Mahony uses the bucket to fill the paddling pool.
He puts 10 full buckets of water in the pool.
How much water is that?

6 The children guess the total number of crisps. There are 60 crisps
in the large packet and 40 in the small packet.
How near is Lucy's guess?

I guess 90

7 Mrs Ryan paid €7 for 2 large packs of burgers.
Both packs cost the same.
What was the cost of each pack?

Burgers
Burgers

8 The children had a jumping game.
Cormac jumped 1 m 10 cm. Anna jumped twice as far.
How far did Anna jump?

9 The barbecue started at half-past 5.
The O'Mahony family left after 2½ hours.
At what time did they leave?

Number problems 16

1 Each pack has 3 pens.

How many pens in 5 packs?

2 Second Class visit a farm. 64 children and 9 adults go on the visit.

How many people go on the visit altogether?

3 Karen has 15 plums.
She gives 4 to David and 4 to Paul.

How many has she left?

4 Eilís puts 13 biscuits on a plate.

Ryan, Andy and Tommy each eat 3 biscuits.
How many are left on the plate?

5 Video Hire has 87 videos. Eleven are borrowed.

How many are left?

6 Darragh has 21 monster cards. He buys 4 more packs, each wi 4 monster cards.

How many monster cards does he have now?

7

When you count up seven 3s followed by two 4s you get to me.

What am I?

Number problems 17

1 The first house is Number 13.
The last house is Number 21.

What is the number of the middle house?

2 An ice-cream man sells 42 cones and 6 lollies.

How many does he sell altogether?

3 Eoin asks 16 friends to come to his party. Seven cannot come as they are ill.

How many come to his party?

4 Each box has 8 muffins.

How many muffins are in 5 boxes?

5 Aoife has a large box of 8 dinosaurs and a small box of 6 dinosaurs.

How many dinosaurs has she?

6 When playing a computer game Stephen scores 62 points and then 19 points.

How many points does he score altogether?

7

I am two numbers. The sum of my two numbers is 100. The difference between my two numbers is 30.

What am I?

Money problems 7

1 David's dad buys a lettuce and some onions.

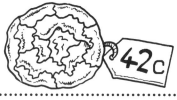 42c

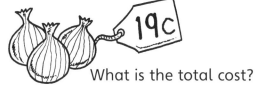 19c

What is the total cost?

2 Each monster costs €5. Grandad buys his 10 grandchildren one each.

€5

What is the total cost of the monsters?

3 Amy takes her purse to the shop. She buys an orange for 21c.

How much has she left?

4 A small box of 10 golf balls cos €40. A large box of 25 golf bal costs twice as much.

 10 golf balls €40

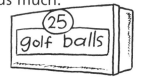 25 golf balls

How much is the box of 25 golf balls?

5 A shop sells cakes for €6 each. Brian's mum wants 5 of them for a party. She has only got €19.

 €6 each

How much more does she need?

6 Renagh shares 14c equally with her brother. She is then given 21c.

How much has Renagh now?

7

I am 7 of the second smallest value coin.

What am I?

Number problems 18

1 There are 4 bars of nut chocolate in each pack.

How many bars are in
6 packs?

2 There are 20 children in Second Class. Each child has 2 balls. They put all the balls equally into 2 bags.

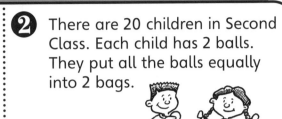

How many balls are in
each bag?

3 There are 10 eggs in a box.

How many boxes are needed for
80 eggs?

4 In a park there are 16 children. Half of them are eating an ice-lolly.

How many children are eating
an ice-lolly?

5 Sarah bakes some cakes.
On each cake she puts 10 jelly sweets.
Altogether she uses 50 jelly sweets.

How many cakes does she bake?

6 Máire's mum buys 20 crayons.
She shares them equally
between Máire and her 3 friends.

How many crayons does
Máire get?

7

*When you halve me,
and then halve me
again, you get 5.*

What am I?

Money problems 8

1 Deirdre has 3 coins in her purse. She spends a quarter of her money on a magazine and another quarter of it on a birthday card.

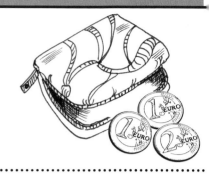

What fraction of her money has she left?
How much has she left?

2 Peter buys 2 CDs.
He pays with a €20 note.

What change does he get?

3 Carol takes 9c to school.
She loses 4c.

How much has she left?

4 Aaron and Kyle get €3.20 each from their aunt.

How much does their aunt give them altogether?

5 Colm has €4 in his money box.
He is given another €3.
He spends €1.50 on a book.

How much has he left?

6 Mary has a €10 note. She buys T-shirt for €6. Her dad gives he €2 toward the T-shirt.

How much has she left?

7  *I am the sum of half the smallest value note and double the smallest value gold coin.* What am I?

Measures problems 2

1 A ferry arrives at half-past ten. The journey took 1½ hours.

At what time did the ferry leave?

2 Krista's mum buys 13 litres of petrol for her own car and 7 litres for Krista's dad's car.

How many litres does she buy?

3 The clock shows the time at which lessons end. Maria leaves school 30 minutes after lessons.

At what time does she leave school?

4 A rain barrel holds 18 litres. When it is full Matt pours it equally into 2 smaller buckets.

How much is in each bucket?

5 At a school fair Hannah sells 16 litres of orange and 4 litres of lemonade.

How much does she sell altogether?

6 On Monday to Thursday Paul's dad comes home at a quarter to 5. On Friday he comes home ½ an hour earlier.

At what time does he come home on Friday?

7

I am between 51 and 79.
I am an even number of 10s.

What am I?

Review problems 6

1 Harry has 75 football cards.
He is given another 11 cards.

How many has he now?

2 Toy robots are sold in boxes of
Ben buys 5 boxes for €14.

How many toy robots does he buy?

3 For a party Ronan's mum buys twelve 2-litre bottles of orange juice.
Nine litres are drunk.

How many litres are left?

4 The clock shows the time Holly's bus leaves the bus station.
She has waited 30 minutes for the bus to leave.

At what time did Holly get to the bus station

5 On Monday 29 people visited a museum in the morning and 33 in the afternoon. Ten more people visited the museum on Sunday than on Monday.

Altogether how many visited on Sunday?

6 Kevin and Carol's dad shares €10 equally between them.
Kevin spends €2.50 of his share on a magazine.

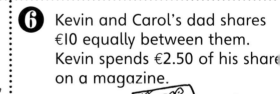

How much has Kevin got left?

7

When you add 6 to me and you take away 4 you get 12.

What am I?